loveactually
THE ORIGINAL SOUNDTRACK

GW00729910

Wise Publications
part of The Music Sales Group

London / New York / Paris / Sydney / Copenhagen / Berlin / Madrid / Tokyo

Published by:
Wise Publications

Exclusive distributors:
Music Sales Limited
Distribution Centre, Newmarket Road,
Bury St Edmunds, Suffolk IP33 3YB, England.
Music Sales Pty Limited
120 Rothschild Avenue, Rosebery, NSW 2018, Australia.

Order No. AM85184
ISBN 0-7119-2696-4
This book © Copyright 2003 by Wise Publications.

Music arrangements by Jack Long.
Music processed by Paul Ewers Music Design.

Printed in the United Kingdom by Caligraving Limited, Thetford, Norfolk.

www.musicsales.com

Your Guarantee of Quality:

As publishers, we strive to produce every book
to the highest commercial standards.

Whilst endeavouring to retain the original running order of the
recorded album, the book has been carefully designed to minimise
awkward page turns and to make playing from it a real pleasure.

Particular care has been given to specifying
acid-free, neutral-sized paper made from pulps which
have not been elemental chlorine bleached.

This pulp is from farmed sustainable forests and
was produced with special regard for the environment.

Throughout, the printing and binding have been
planned to ensure a sturdy, attractive publication
which should give years of enjoyment.

If your copy fails to meet our high standards,
please inform us and we will gladly replace it.

Jump (For My Love)

Words & Music by Gary Skardina, Marti Sharron & Stephen Mitchell

1. Your eyes___ tell___ me how you

3

want me; I can feel__ it in your heart - beat.

I know__ you like__ what you see.

2. Hold me,__ I'll give__ you all that you need.
(3.) told me__ I'm the on - ly wo - man for you;

Wrap__ your love a - round me. You're so ex - cit - ed I can
no - bo - dy does it like I do. Then make a move be - fore you

4

and feel___ my touch.___ (Jump) If you wan - na taste my
kiss - es in the night, then___ jump___ for___ my love.___
I know my heart can make you hap - py.___ (Jump in.) You know these arms, they
fill you up. (Jump.) If you wan - na taste my kiss - es in the night, then___

jump_____ for____ my love._____

3. You

When you__ are

next_____ to me,_____ oh I come a - live.

Your love burns in -

Christmas Is All Around

Words & Music by Reg Presley
Adaptation of the song "Love Is All Around"

You know I love Christ - mas, I al - ways will;
(3° instrumental)

my mind's made up by the way that I feel.

There's no be - gin - ning, there'll be no end, 'cause on Christ - mas you

To Coda ⊕   **1.**   **2.**

can de - pend.   3. You   *D.S. al Coda*

Songbird

Words & Music by Christine McVie

(Verse 2 see block lyric)

1. For _____ you_____ there'll_____ be_____ no cry - ing._____

For_____ you_____

the sun_____ will be shin - - ing_____ cos I

feel that when____ I'm with you it's al - right._____

____ I know____ it's____ right._____ And the song-

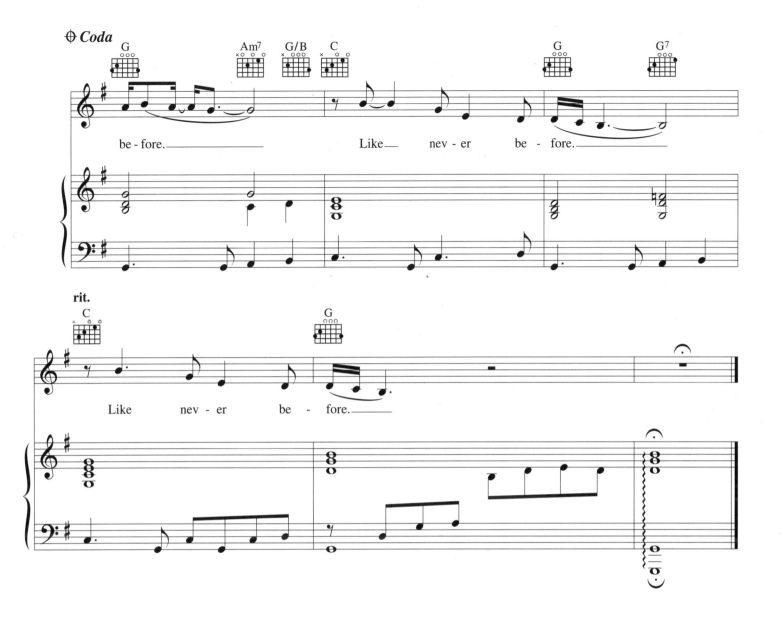

Verse 2:
To you I would give the world
To you I'd never be cold
'Cause I feel that when I'm with you
It's alright
I know it's right.

And the songbirds keep singing *etc.*

Too Lost In You

Words & Music by Diane Warren

The Trouble With Love Is

Words & Music by Evan Rogers, Carl Sturken & Kelly Clarkson

1. Love can be a ma-ny splen-doured thing, can't de-ny the joy it brings:
2. Now I was once a fool, it's true, I played the game by all the rules;

tear you up in-side,_____ make your heart be-lieve a_____ lie._____ It's

strong-er than your pride._____ The trou-ble with love_ is_____ it does-n't

care how fast you fall,_____ and you can't re-fuse_ the call._____ See, you've

1. got no say at all,_____ oh._____ **2.** got no say at all._____

N.C. N.C. N.C. N.C.

Ev-'ry-time I turn a-round,_____ I think I've_ got it all____ fig-ured out. **3**

My heart keeps call-ing, and I keep on fall-ing ov - er and ov-er a-gain._____

This sad sto-ry al-ways ends_ the_ same:_____ me_ stand-ing in the pour-ing rain._

***D.S.** repeat chorus to fade*

It seems,_ no mat-ter what I do,_____ it tears_ my heart in two. The trou-ble with

Here With Me

Words & Music by Dido Armstrong, Paul Statham & Pascal Gabriel

33

Turn Me On

Words & Music by John D. Loudermilk

And with a tear in my eye,____ give me the sweet - est good - bye____

that I ev - er did re - ceive_____

Push - ing for - ward___ and arch - ing

back bring___ me clos - er___ to

feel,_____ feel._____

Instrumental

Wherever You Will Go

Words & Music by Aaron Kamin & Alex Band

-ev - er___ you___ will go.___

I'll go wher - ev - er___ you___ will go.___

Verse 2:
And maybe I'll find out a way to make it back some day
To want you, to guide you through the darkest of your days
If a great wave shall fall
It'll fall upon us all
Well then I hope there's someone out there
Who can bring me back to you.

If I could then I would *etc.*

I'll See It Through

Words & Music by John McElhone, Sharleen Spiteri & Guy Chambers

1. When you touch me,— I feel there's no-thing you can
(2.) close my eyes— and think of you, it takes me

do to turn— me a-way. And I
plac-es that I've nev-er seen. And the

right___ thing to do,_____ and I'll___ see it through._____

Both Sides Now

Words & Music by Joni Mitchell

1. Bows and flows of an - gel hair,___ and ice - cream cas - tles
2. Moons and Junes and fer - ris wheels,___ the diz - zy danc - ing
3. Tears and fears and feel - ing proud___ to say "I love you"

So many things, I would have done, but clouds got in my
And if you care, don't let them know; don't give your self a-
But some-thing's lost, but some-thing's gained in liv-ing ev-'ry

way. I've looked at clouds from both sides now,
-way. I've looked at love from both sides now,
day. I've looked at life from both sides now,

from up and down, and still some-how it's cloud il-lu-sions
from give and take, and still some-how it's love's il-lu-sions that
from win and lose, and still some-how it's life's il-lu-sions

Take Me As I Am

Words & Music by Wyclef Jean, Jerry Duplessis & Sharissa Dawes

got caught___   I sent you a doz-en of ro - ses.   You sent
came off rude;   but still you of love me. I   know I get on your

them back and told me "Go to hell!" But___ girl you know that   you take me as___ I am;___
nerves some-times,___ and I don't___ know why,   you take me as___ I am;___

ev - en tho' my___ fam___ don't___ un - der -
ev - en when my___ girls___ can't___ un - der -

- stand   why I put that rock up-on___ your hand:___
- stand   I choose you as___ my man___

62

la - dy.___ (G) My ba - by (B) You're my ba - by. (G) My hon - ey.___

(B) You dose___ in the breeze that I feel when I'm blow - ing my trees a - long.___

(G) You're the sun that shines when the dark - ness strikes at night.

(B) You're the love of my life, you're my girl, you're my wife. (G) Yes I am. You're

67

All I Want For Christmas Is You

Words & Music by Mariah Carey & Walter Afanasieff

make my wish come true,_____ all I want for Christ - mas

is_____ you._____

_____ 1. I don't want a lot____
(Verse 2 see block lyric)

_____ for Christ - mas, there is just one thing___ I need,___ and

All the lights are shin-ing so bright-ly ev-'ry-where and the sound of child-ren's laugh-ter fills the air and ev-'ry-one is sing-ing, I hear those sleigh bells ring-ing

Verse 2:
I won't ask for much this Christmas
I won't even ask for snow,
I'm just gonna keep on waiting
Underneath the mistletoe.
I won't make a list and send it
To the North Pole for Saint Nick,
I won't even stay awake
To hear those magic reindeers click.
'Cause I just want you here tonight
Holding on to me so tight,
What more can I do,
Baby all I want for Christmas is you.

Verse 3:
I don't want a lot for Christmas
This is all I'm asking for,
I just want to see my baby
Standing right outside my door.
Oh I just want you for my own,
More than you could ever know,
Make my wish come true,
Baby all I want for Christmas is you.

73

God Only Knows

Words & Music by Brian Wilson & Tony Asher

I'll make you so_____ sure a - bout it.

God on - ly knows__

To Coda ⊕

__ what I'd be with - out_____ you.

Ah,_____ ah._____ Do do do do do do

Verse 2:
If you should ever leave me
Though life would still go on, believe me
The world could show nothing to me
So what good would living do me?
God only knows what I'd be without you.

Verse 3 as Verse 2

77

Sometimes

Words & Music by Gabrielle & Jonathan Shorten

Repeat to fade

83

All You Need Is Love

Words & Music by John Lennon & Paul McCartney

Love is all__ you need.__

(Instrumental)

All you need is__ love.__

All you need is__ love,__

86

Love is all___ you need.___ Love is all___ you need.___

Love is all___ you need.___ Love is all___ you need.___

Love is all___ you need.___ Love is all___ you need.___

Love is all_____ you need._____

PM's Love Theme

By Craig Armstrong

Glasgow Love Theme

By Craig Armstrong

Portugese Love Theme

By Craig Armstrong

2/09(168961)